Music Theory Practice Papers 2017

ABRSM's *Music Theory Practice Papers 2017* are adapted from the 2017 Music Theory exam papers. Some questions are the same as those used in recent exams. Others ha\ been adapted to reflect the new question types being used in some parts of the Grade . .. .. papers from 1 January 2018. These include multiple-choice questions for some terms and signs and questions with a clearer layout.

The *Music Theory Practice Papers 2017* for Grades 1 to 5 do not include rhythm-writing, word-setting, melody-writing or SATB short/open score questions, as these no longer appear in exams.

Music Theory exams – Grades 1 to 5, from 1 January 2018

Although we have made some small changes to Music Theory exams at Grades 1 to 5, the knowledge needed by candidates remains the same. ABRSM's existing music theory books continue to be valid and useful resources for candidates preparing for exams.

Find out more about our Grade 1 to 5 Music Theory exams at **www.abrsm.org/theory**.

Theory Paper   Grade 5   2017   A

Duration 2 hours

TOTAL MARKS
100

This paper contains SEVEN questions, ALL of which should be answered.
Write your answers on this paper – no others will be accepted.
Answers must be written clearly and neatly – otherwise marks may be lost.

1 (a) Look at the following extract and then answer the questions below.

15

Karg-Elert, *Fable* for piano, Op. 32 No. 2

(i) The extract begins on the first beat of the bar and contains some changes of time signature. Put in the correct time signatures at the two places marked *.

(4)

(ii) Rewrite the first note of bar 3 (marked ↓) so that it sounds at the same pitch, but using the tenor C clef. Remember to put in the clef and the key signature.

(3)

(iii) Write as a breve (double whole-note) an enharmonic equivalent of the last note of the extract.

(2)

(b) Look at the following extract and then answer the question below.

Haydn, Keyboard Sonata, Hob. XVI/9

Describe the chords marked **A**, **B** and **C** as I, II, IV or V. Also indicate whether the lowest note of the chord is the root (a), 3rd (b) or 5th (c). The key is F major.

Chord **A** (bar 1)   ....   (2)

Chord **B** (bar 2)   ....   (2)

Chord **C** (bar 3)   ....   (2)

2 (a) Describe fully (e.g. major 2nd, perfect 5th) each of these melodic intervals.

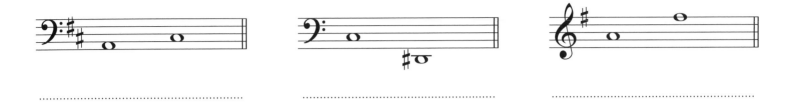

....

(b) **After** each of these notes write a **higher** note to form the named **melodic** interval.

augmented 4th   perfect 11th

3 These are the actual sounds made by a clarinet in B♭. Rewrite the passage as it would appear for the player to read, that is, transpose it **up** a major 2nd. Remember to put in the new key signature and add any necessary accidentals.

Bärmann, Clarinet Sonata, Op. 31

4 Look at this extract from a piano sonatina by Vanhal and then answer the questions that follow.

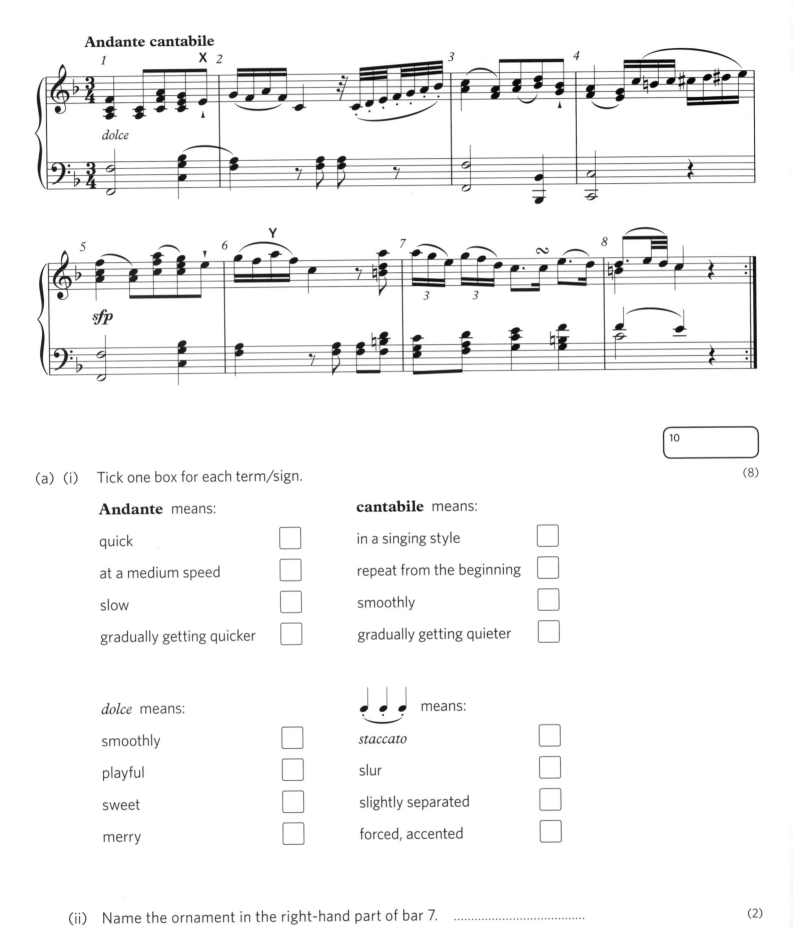

(a) (i) Tick one box for each term/sign. (8)

Andante means:

quick ☐

at a medium speed ☐

slow ☐

gradually getting quicker ☐

cantabile means:

in a singing style ☐

repeat from the beginning ☐

smoothly ☐

gradually getting quieter ☐

dolce means:

smoothly ☐

playful ☐

sweet ☐

merry ☐

♩♩♩ means:

staccato ☐

slur ☐

slightly separated ☐

forced, accented ☐

(ii) Name the ornament in the right-hand part of bar 7. .... (2)

(b) (i) Complete this statement:

All the notes in bars 7–8 can be found in the key of ....   (2)

   (ii) Below the staves write Ic–V ($^6_4$ $^5_3$) under the **two** chords next to each other in bars 1–4 where this progression occurs. Remember that the key is F major.   (2)

   (iii) Give the technical names (e.g. tonic, dominant) of the two notes in the right-hand part marked **X** and **Y**.

   X (bar 1)   ....   (2)

   Y (bar 6)   ....   (2)

   (iv) Draw a bracket (⌐‾‾‾⌐) over **five** notes next to each other that form part of a chromatic scale.   (2)

(c) (i) Name one similarity and one difference **in the right-hand part** between bar 1 and bar 5.

   Similarity   ....   (1)

   Difference   ....   (1)

   (ii) Name a standard orchestral instrument that could play the right-hand part of bar 7 so that it sounds at the same pitch, and state the family of instruments to which it belongs.

   Instrument   ....   Family   ....   (4)

   (iii) Underline **one** instrument in the list below that is a transposing instrument.

   cello   timpani   viola   clarinet   (2)

   (iv) Answer TRUE or FALSE to this statement:

   An oboist may sometimes be asked to play 'pizzicato'.   ....   (2)

5 (a) Put accidentals in front of the notes that need them to form the scale of F **melodic** minor. Do **not** use a key signature.

(b) Using semibreves (whole notes), write one octave **ascending** of the **chromatic** scale that begins on the given note. Remember to put in all necessary accidentals.

6 Look at this extract and then answer the questions that follow.

(a) Tick one box for each term. (4)

con dolore means:		*incalzando* means:	
with force	☐	getting quicker	☐
with love	☐	getting slower	☐
with grief	☐	playful, joking	☐
with determination	☐	dying away	☐

(b) Give the technical names (e.g. tonic, dominant) of the two notes in bar 5 and bar 6 marked **X** and **Y**. The key is G minor.

X .... (2)

Y .... (2)

8

(c) Rewrite bar 1 using notes of **twice the value**. Remember to put in the new time signature.

(4)

(d) Rewrite the first note of bar 7 (marked ↓) so that it sounds at the same pitch, but using the alto C clef. Remember to put in the clef and the key signature.

(3)

7 Indicate suitable progressions for two cadences in the following melody by writing I, II, IV or V in the boxes underneath the stave. Use **one** chord per box.

10

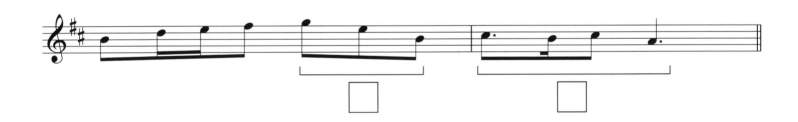

Theory Paper   Grade 5   2017   B

Duration 2 hours

TOTAL MARKS
100

This paper contains SEVEN questions, ALL of which should be answered.
Write your answers on this paper – no others will be accepted.
Answers must be written clearly and neatly – otherwise marks may be lost.

1 (a) Rewrite the following extract with the notes correctly grouped (beamed).

15

J. S. Bach, Cantata *Bereitet die Wege*, BWV 132

etc.

etc.

(7)

(b) Look at the following extract and then answer the questions below.

T. Kirchner, *Albumblatt*, Op. 14 No. 2

etc.

(i) Tick one box for each term/sign. (6)

Sehr means:		**ruhig** means:		𝟪ᵛᵃ‑‑‑‑‑‑‑‑‑┐ means:	
somewhat, rather	☐	peaceful	☐	perform an octave lower	☐
very	☐	tender	☐	pause on the note or rest	☐
always	☐	loving	☐	perform an octave higher	☐
without	☐	hurrying	☐	perform the notes smoothly	☐

(ii) Describe the time signature as: simple or compound .... (1)

duple, triple or quadruple .... (1)

2 Describe fully (e.g. major 2nd, perfect 5th) each of these melodic intervals.

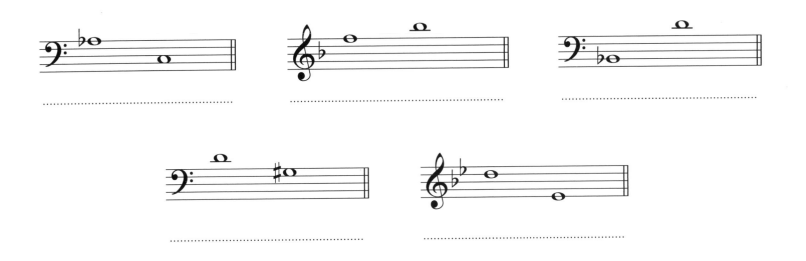

....

....

3 The following melody is written for trumpet in B♭. Transpose it **down** a major 2nd, as it will sound at concert pitch. Remember to put in the new key signature and add any necessary accidentals.

Brandt, No. 23 from 34 Studies for trumpet

4 Look at this extract from a sonata for bassoon and piano by Saint-Saëns and then answer the questions that follow.

(a) (i) Tick one box. (2)

scherzando means:

spirited ☐

simple, plain ☐

sad, sorrowful ☐

playful, joking ☐

(ii) Add the correct rest(s) at the place marked ✳ to complete bar 8 of the bassoon part. (2)

(iii) Describe the chords in the piano part marked $\boxed{A}$, $\boxed{B}$ and $\boxed{C}$ as I, II, IV or V. Also indicate whether the lowest note of the chord is the root (a), 3rd (b) or 5th (c). The key is E minor.

Chord **A** (bar 4) ....   (2)

Chord **B** (bar 7) ....   (2)

Chord **C** (bar 7) ....   (2)

(b) (i) Rewrite the last two notes in the bassoon part of bar 7 (marked ⌐⌐) so that they sound at the same pitch, but using the tenor C clef. Remember to put in the clef and the key signature.

| 10 |

(4)

(ii) Give the technical names (e.g. tonic, dominant) of the two notes in the bassoon part marked **X** and **Y**. Remember that the key is E minor.

X (bar 4) ....   (2)

Y (bar 5) ....   (2)

(iii) Which other key has the same key signature as E minor?

Key: ....   (2)

(c) (i) Answer TRUE or FALSE to these statements:

| 10 |

The bassoon is a non-transposing instrument. ....   (2)

The bassoon is a single-reed instrument. ....   (2)

(ii) The bassoon is a member of the woodwind family of orchestral instruments. Name a standard orchestral instrument from a **different** family that could play the bassoon part of the extract so that it sounds at the same pitch, and state the family of instruments to which it belongs.

Instrument ....   Family ....   (4)

(iii) Underline **one** of the percussion instruments in the list below that produces sounds of definite pitch.

tambourine   glockenspiel   castanets   triangle   (2)

13

5 (a) Write the key signature of four sharps and then one octave **ascending** of the major scale with that key signature. Use semibreves (whole notes) and begin on the tonic.

[10]

(b) Using semibreves (whole notes), write one octave **descending** of the **harmonic** minor scale that begins on the given note. Do **not** use a key signature but put in all necessary accidentals.

6 Look at this extract and then answer the questions that follow.

[15]

(a) Tick one box for each term.

(4)

Mässig means:		*süss* means:	
at a moderate speed	☐	smoothly	☐
mournful	☐	simple	☐
playful, merry	☐	sad	☐
lively	☐	sweet	☐

(b) Give the technical names (e.g. tonic, dominant) of the two notes in bar 1 marked **X** and **Y**. The key is G major.

X .... (2)

Y .... (2)

(c) Rewrite bar 1 using notes of **twice the value**. Remember to put in the new time signature.

(4)

(d) Write as a breve (double whole-note) an enharmonic equivalent of the first note of the extract.

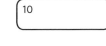

(2)

(e) Give the letter name of the **highest** note in the melody.   ....

(1)

7 Indicate suitable progressions for two cadences in the following melody by writing I, II, IV or V in the boxes underneath the stave. Use **one** chord per box.

10

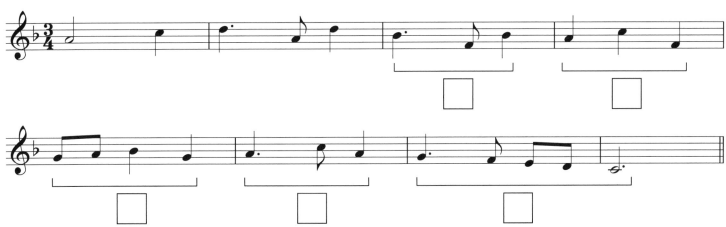

Theory Paper   Grade 5   2017   C

Duration 2 hours

TOTAL MARKS 100

This paper contains SEVEN questions, ALL of which should be answered.
Write your answers on this paper – no others will be accepted.
Answers must be written clearly and neatly – otherwise marks may be lost.

1 (a) Look at the following extract and then answer the questions below.

[15]

Cédez peu à peu

Chausson, *Pièce* for cello and piano, Op. 39

etc.

(i)   The extract begins on the first beat of the bar. Put in the correct time signature.   (2)

(ii)   Tick one box for each term.   (4)

Cédez means:		**peu** means:	
hurrying	☐	more	☐
in strict time	☐	enough, sufficiently	☐
yield, relax the speed	☐	less	☐
with determination	☐	little	☐

(iii)   How many demisemiquavers (32nd notes) are
        the tied notes in bar 1 (marked ↑) worth in total?   ....   (2)

(b) Look at the following extract and then answer the questions that follow.

Mozart, Piano Sonata in A, K. 331

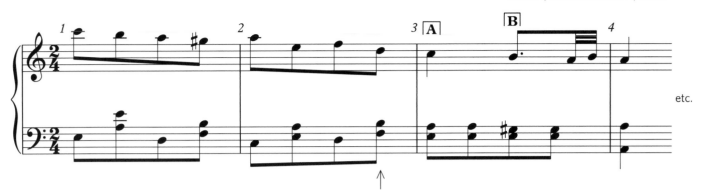

etc.

(i) Describe the chords marked **A** and **B** as I, II, IV or V. Also indicate whether the lowest note of the chord is the root (a), 3rd (b) or 5th (c). The key is A minor.

Chord **A** (bar 3)   ....   (2)

Chord **B** (bar 3)   ....   (2)

(ii) Rewrite the last left-hand chord of bar 2 (marked ↑) so that it sounds at the same pitch, but using the alto C clef. Remember to put in the clef.

(3)

2 (a) Describe fully (e.g. major 2nd, perfect 5th) each of these melodic intervals.   [10]

   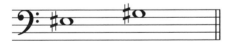   

....

(b) **After** each of these notes write a **higher** note to form the named **melodic** interval.

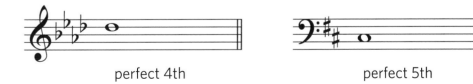

perfect 4th   perfect 5th

17

3 Look at this extract, which is adapted from a keyboard piece by J. S. Bach, and then answer the questions that follow.

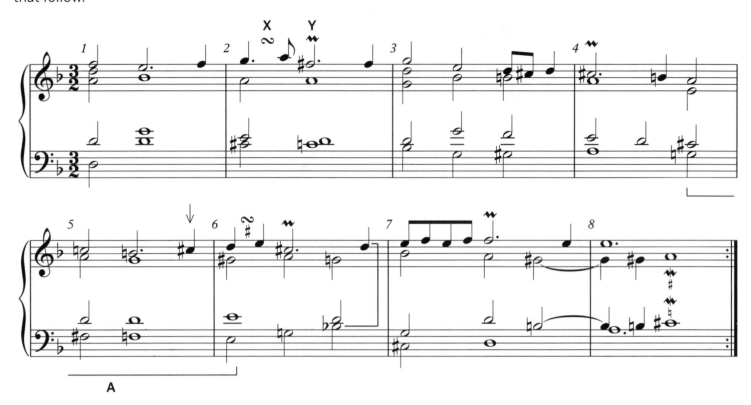

(a) (i) **Mark clearly on the music**, using the appropriate capital letter for identification, one example of each of the following. Also give the bar number(s) of each of your answers, as shown in the answer to **A**.

   A   in the left-hand part, four notes next to each other that
   form part of a chromatic scale (mark ⌐A⌐ under the notes).   Bars ....4–6.....

   B   in bars 1–4 of the right-hand part, a subdominant
   note in the key of D minor (circle the note concerned).   Bar ....   (2)

   C   in bars 1–4, a supertonic chord in first inversion (IIb)
   in the key of D minor (circle the notes concerned).   Bar ....   (2)

   D   a tie in the left-hand part.   Bars ....   (2)

   (ii)   Write as a breve (double whole-note) an enharmonic equivalent of the last note in the
   top right-hand part of bar 5 (marked ↓).

   (2)

   (iii)   Describe the time signature as: simple or compound   ....   (1)

   duple, triple or quadruple   ....   (1)

(b) (i) Give the meaning of : ‖ (bar 8). .... (2)

(ii) Name the two ornaments marked **X** and **Y** in bar 2.

X .... (2)

Y .... (2)

(iii) Describe fully the bracketed harmonic interval in
bar 6 (top right-hand and bottom left-hand notes). .... (2)

(iv) Give the time name (e.g. crotchet or
quarter note) of the **longest** note in the extract. .... (2)

(c) (i) Name a standard orchestral instrument that could play the bottom left-hand notes of
bars 1–4 so that they sound at the same pitch, and state the family of instruments to which
it belongs.

Instrument .... Family .... (4)

(ii) Now name a **different** family of standard orchestral instruments and state its
highest-sounding member.

Family .... Instrument .... (4)

(iii) Answer TRUE or FALSE to this statement:

A pianist might be asked to play 'sul ponticello'. .... (2)

4 (a) Write one octave **descending** of the scale of B major. Do **not** use a key signature but put in all necessary accidentals. Use semibreves (whole notes) and begin on the tonic.

10

(b) Write the key signature of four flats and then one octave **ascending** of the **melodic** minor scale with that key signature. Use semibreves (whole notes), begin on the tonic and remember to put in any necessary accidentals.

5 The following melody is written for horn in F. Transpose it **down** a perfect 5th, as it will sound at concert pitch. Do **not** use a key signature but remember to put in all necessary accidentals.

10

Belloli, No. 5 from Eight Studies for horn

etc.

6 Look at this extract and then answer the questions that follow.

15

(a) Tick one box for each item. (6)

Adagietto means:

gradually getting slower ☐

at a medium speed ☐

very slow, solemn ☐

rather slow ☐

alla misura means:

in the style of a march ☐

in strict time ☐

at the same speed ☐

in free time ☐

sotto voce means:

dying away ☐

resonant, with rich tone ☐

in an undertone ☐

singing ☐

(b) Give the technical names (e.g. tonic, dominant) of the two notes in bar 2 marked **X** and **Y**.
The key is C minor.

X .... (2)

Y .... (2)

(c) Complete this statement:

All the notes in bars 5–6 can be found in the key of .... (2)

(d) Which other key has the same key signature as C minor? .... (2)

(e) Give the letter name of the **highest** note in the melody. .... (1)

---

7 Indicate suitable progressions for two cadences in the following melody by writing I, II, IV or V
in the boxes underneath the stave. Use **one** chord per box.

[10]

Theory Paper   Grade 5   2017   S

Duration 2 hours

This paper contains **SEVEN** questions, **ALL** of which should be answered.
Write your answers on this paper – no others will be accepted.
Answers must be written clearly and neatly – otherwise marks may be lost.

TOTAL MARKS
100

1 (a) Look at the following extract and then answer the questions below.

15

Stravinsky, *The Rite of Spring*

   (i)   The extract begins on the first beat of the bar and contains some changes of time signature.
         Put in the correct time signatures at the three places marked ∗.   (6)

   (ii) Rewrite the first two notes of bar 3 (marked ⌐⌐) so that they sound at the same pitch, but
         using the alto C clef. Remember to put in the clef.

(3)

(b) Look at the following extract and then answer the question below.

Mozart, Piano Sonata in A minor, K. 310

etc.

Describe the chords marked ⟦**A**⟧, ⟦**B**⟧ and ⟦**C**⟧ as I, II, IV or V. Also indicate whether the lowest note of
the chord is the root (a), 3rd (b) or 5th (c). The key is F major.

Chord **A** (bar 2)   ....   (2)

Chord **B** (bar 4)   ....   (2)

Chord **C** (bar 4)   ....   (2)

2 Describe fully (e.g. major 2nd, perfect 5th) each of these melodic intervals.

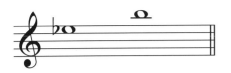

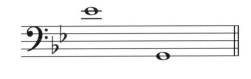

....

....

3 The following melody is written for clarinet in A. Transpose it **down** a minor 3rd, as it will sound at concert pitch. Do **not** use a key signature but remember to put in all necessary sharp, flat or natural signs.

Honegger, Sonatine for clarinet and piano

4 Look at this extract from a song by Schubert and then answer the questions that follow.

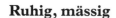

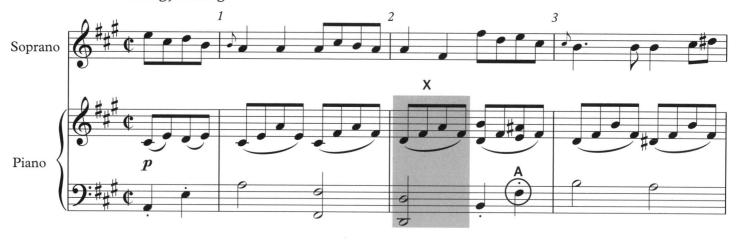

etc.

(a) (i) **Mark clearly on the music**, using the appropriate capital letter for identification, one example of each of the following. Also give the bar number of each of your answers, as shown in the answer to **A**.

A in the left-hand piano part, a note that is marked to be played short and detached (circle the note concerned).   Bar ....2....

B in bars 1–4 of the right-hand piano part, three notes next to each other that form the supertonic chord in first inversion (II b) in the key of A major (circle the notes concerned.)   Bar ....   (2)

C in bars 1–4 of the soprano part, a note that is the submediant of A major (circle the note concerned).   Bar ....   (2)

D in the soprano part, a note that is an enharmonic equivalent of A♭ (circle the note concerned).   Bar ....   (2)

(ii) Rewrite the last left-hand piano chord of the extract so that it sounds at the same pitch, but using the tenor C clef. Remember to put in the clef and the key signature.

(4)

(b) (i) Tick one box for each term. (4)

Ruhig means: **mässig** means:

simple ☐   lively ☐

tender ☐   playful, merry ☐

plaintive ☐   at a moderate speed ☐

peaceful ☐   in a military style ☐

(ii) The extract begins in the key of A major.
Which other key has the same key signature? .... (2)

(iii) Describe the chords (shaded) in the piano part marked **X** and **Y** as I, II, IV or V.
Also indicate whether the lowest note of the chord is the root (a), 3rd (b) or 5th (c).
Remember that the key is A major.

Chord **X** (bar 2) .... (2)

Chord **Y** (bar 4) .... (2)

(c) (i) Name the ornament in the soprano part of bar 3. .... (2)

(ii) Give the name of the voice part that lies
between tenor and bass in vocal range. .... (2)

(iii) Name a standard orchestral instrument that could play the soprano part of the extract so that
it sounds at the same pitch, and state the family of instruments to which it belongs.

Instrument ....   Family .... (4)

(iii) Underline **one** instrument in the list below that is **not** a transposing instrument.

trumpet   double bass   bassoon   clarinet (2)

5 (a) Put accidentals in front of the notes that need them to form the scale of F♯ major. Do **not** use a key signature.

(b) Using semibreves (whole notes), write one octave **descending** of the **harmonic** minor scale that has the given key signature. Begin on the tonic and remember to put in any necessary accidentals.

6 Look at this extract and then answer the questions that follow.

(a) Tick one box for each term. (6)

scherzoso means:		*affettuoso* means:		*affrettando* means:	
spirited	☐	with passion	☐	bold, strong	☐
sweet	☐	pleasant	☐	hurrying	☐
forced, accented	☐	simple, plain	☐	heavy	☐
playful, joking	☐	tenderly	☐	sad, sorrowful	☐

(b) Rewrite bar 4 using notes of twice the value. Remember to put in the new time signature.

(4)